SANDPILES

Poems by Zachary M. Corsa
Paintings by E.M. Corsa

Special thanks to manufacturing agent, Laura Livingston and graphic designer, Katherine Payne.

Pubished by Aerial Perspective   Robert V. Drapala Publishing

428 Cripps Drive, Mount Holly, New Jersey 08060

www.aerialperspective.com

ISBN 0-9660586-9-0

Printed in China

Aunt Connie,
with you in mind.

Deep beneath the pulsing waves
an old salt lives within his cave.
It's built of seaglass, shells and things,
of catfish whiskers, pi-rat rings.
And if you visit him sometime,
he'll tell you tales of ocean lives
and how it is beneath the sea
for a grizzled fish like he.
He'll light his pipe and draw you near,
so listen closely if you dare.
And when he's done this ancient chap
will show you all his treasure maps
and coins and jewels and books in tatters,
all from the bottom he has gathered.
And if you wish to hear some more
he'll start again with ocean lore.
So gather round you fine young mates,
the story's starting, don't be late.
For here you'll find all things of wonder,
like fish that fly and rats who plunder,
crabs that scare and beach bugs too,
on golden sand and sea of blue.

Atop the high and sandy dunes
beach buggies sit a thinkin',
planning what their picnic needs
and what they will be drinkin'.

Bug juice, cake and sandwiches,
but how to stop a crowd
from eating everything they bring,
AHA! No ants allowed!

Apple, peach, grape and berry,
jellyfish are sometimes scary.
But add some bread and peanut butter,
and their hearts are all aflutter.

Ask them nicely and they will share
all these tasty treats of theirs.
But when you go, they'll make it known,
Next time, bring some of your own!

5

Gathered behind seashell drapes,
trying dresses, suits and capes,

these models stalk the runway of
a summer shoreline stretched above

the water of entrancing blue,
flamingos that are on the move,

with pretty pink and ruffled down,
feathered boas on their gowns.

The mermaid cat is not so cursed
as others maybe like her.
For she is queen of sandy shores
and everyone abides her.

They bring her treats on which to dine,
no sardines from a store.
Only freshest meals allowed
at this feline madam's door.

Her scales, the finest emerald shade,
her eyes the color blue;
her fishy tail, her furry paws,
are sure to enchant you.

But when you are a guest of hers
be sure to bring along,
some legs of crab or other dishes
soon to become — gone!

10

Every year they make their tracks
to the edges of their maps,
far from winter's stormy gale,
upon the ocean, they set sail.

Bunnies in bikini-wear
gathered nearly everywhere,
picnic baskets near at hand,
beach umbrella set in sand.

Whiskered noses pointed high
to the sun and cloudless sky,
these ladies lounge until the shift
of summer back to winter drifts.

Yet soon they will return again
when calendars reveal the end
of February wind and cold,
they'll set off for that beach of gold.

Here where turtles gather close
to listen to the magic notes,
drums are pounding, strings are strumming,
turtles all around are humming.

Conga lines and mermaid songs
encourage all to dance along.
It's a party all can share.
We hope that you will join us there.

13

Under turning waves of blue
the ocean circus waits for you.
And what of course is its attraction?
The seahorse carousel in action!

But for admission when you're greeted,
a sand dollar or two is needed.
Music, bubbles, lights and rings,
the seahorse to his pole will cling.

Different colors of every hue,
why not mount the one that's blue?
So take a spin and grab a ring,
the perfect time to have a fling.

# 16

REGAL

Perched atop his piling throne
the regal seagull rests alone,
as king of all the ocean tide
and every creature by his side.
With goldfish trident kept at wing
he fills his head with stately things,
and with a crown of seaweed jewels
he makes the plans and sets the rules.
The fish and squid and octopus,
his charges dare not make a fuss.
Rewards are great for friends of kings,
like necklaces and starfish rings.
He's listened to and always near
if anyone should shout a cheer
for feathered lords of seaside lands,
this bird of glory has command!

17

18

Look! Your map is upside down.
We'll never find that treasure now!

The cheese is molding 'neath the sand
while we sit here, swords in hand,
wondering which path to take
through this dreary island-scape.
And tribal cats that prowl so deep
are hunting for us while we sleep.

Oh rats like us will never do,
that's why we left our pi-rat school.
We're the ones who've never heard
our silent parrot utter words.
The only way we'll find that bait
is through blind luck or pure mistake!

But still there's hope here to be found;
why can't we turn our map around?

High up off the ocean floor
so their shells don't get too sore,
oysters sprawl and lounge like cads
while hidden deep within the pads,
are pearls of wisdom shining bright
to take out when it's dark at night.
Like underwater stars they'll be,
the pearls will help the oysters see.

21

Like acrobats through sky they soar,
attached by ropes to kites and more,
and on balloons they sail the clouds,
until the night when they set down.

Into the coral they retreat,
until the daylight stirs them deep,
they rise like bubbles with the dawn
to test the wind and then fly on.

Below the waves, beneath the sea,
with nets and ropes he waits for me,
while sitting on the bottom.

In water only to my knee,
his slippery smile, full of glee,
while waiting on the bottom.

But undertoads do not scare me,
and never can I let them be,
while resting on the bottom.

With pail in hand, a merry spree,
I reach down under, now I see,
Kerplunk! I finally caught him!

25

Here he slaves to find the words,
expressing all so she may learn,
of how devoted he can be,
to a jellyfish like she.

For many days and many nights,
he sits with pad in hands and writes,
and yet the words all wash away,
the ink he uses cannot say,
what hides within his octo-heart,
so her romancing he may start.

Invisible, his letter dashed,
he sets about a plan to hatch.
At last he sets a rapid pace,
to tell his dearest face to face.

Do not fear the beach at night,
for if you dare, you'll find a sight
unlike the ones you've seen before,
the ghost crabs hide upon the shore.

Clad in robes of phantom-white,
ghost crabs will not cause a fright,
or sneak up close to shout out BOO
to scare the nightlights out of you.

So if you spy a ghost crab near
remember this and make it clear:
"I will not fear these night-time creatures,
like monsters from a double-feature."

These shy crustaceans leave you alone
when nestled in their beachy home,
and in the day they don't seem scary
their costumes gone, they will not tarry.

29

So ends the day upon the shore
with one more treat for you in store.
Look above to starlit sky,
and see the starfish soaring high,
pulling stars and galaxies,
and a wish for you and me.
A starfish's work is only done
when morning brings the rising sun.
So make your haste to bed young ones,
the day is fading, my work's near done.
Until the next day ye draw near,
I promise to be waiting here
with further tales of fishy friends
and all your old pals back again.
But now I sleep in Old Salt's Cave,
good night young ones, you've been so brave.
So do not linger when I'm done,
the ocean's rest has just begun.
And you had best be off yourselves,
just don't forget your special shells.
I leave you now, and thanks for all,
and you my visitors, stand tall.
The world awaits you far from here,
the sea awakens without fear.
I'll look-out for your swift return,
you still have so much left to learn.
And there's always things to do,
here beneath our sea of blue.